Our essay at the back of this book offers you information about language, child
together. It offers a view of the classroom as a launching pad to human greatn

SOUNDS
Around
the Mountain

By **Bill Martin Jr**
with **Peggy Brogan** and
John Archambault

DLM®
One DLM Park • Allen, Texas 75002

The cover and title page of this book, like those of the other big books, were illustrated by Steven Kellogg. You probably have many of his books in your school or classroom library. If possible, have those books available for comparison. The more children know about people who helped put the book together, the more apt they are to become book lovers.

This book contains many favorite poems and songs that the children will want to hear, sing, and read over and over and over.

Think of this book as an anthology. Any place is a good place to start. The book is also an "art gallery." Let the children pick out the illustrations they like best and talk about them.

Whenever you read a selection aloud to communicate its literary pleasure, read it without interruption. After the reading is the time to turn back, to point out, and to invite comments.

She'll Be Comin' Round the Mountain

an old song

illustrated by

Steven Kellogg

She'll be comin' round the mountain
when she comes, *when she comes!*
She'll be comin' round the mountain
when she comes, *when she comes!*

She'll be comin' round the mountain,
She'll be comin' round the mountain,
She'll be comin' round the mountain
    when she comes, *when she comes!*

Daydreaming over this picture lets you hears the gallop of horses and the jingle of harnesses. It also invites you to explore all kinds of story meanings and personal feelings.

She'll be drivin' six white horses
when she comes, *hoa back!*
She'll be drivin' six white horses
when she comes, *hoa back!*

She'll be drivin' six white horses,
She'll be drivin' six white horses,
She'll be drivin' six white horses
  when she comes, *hoa back!*

There she is with a great box of . . . . The children can tell you what's in the box. Your children, just as the children in the story, *have* to know what's in there. They can't rest until they do!

We'll all have chicken and dumplin's
when she comes, *yum, yum!*
We'll all have chicken and dumplin's
when she comes, *yum, yum!*

We'll all have chicken and dumplin's,
We'll all have chicken and dumplin's,
We'll all have chicken and dumplin's
when she comes, *yum, yum!*

If you haven't met Noodles before, make his acquaintance. He's a character in all of the **Sounds of Language** books, representing the essence of childhood. Children strongly identify with his humor, his curiosity, and his ability to work his way through the adult world with minimum friction and maximum pleasure.

Embedded in this dialogue between Noodles and Reinbow is an echo of "The Night Before Christmas" leading to an allusion to "Humpty Dumpty." Not all children will recognize this, but if you read "The Night Before Christmas" or "Humpty Dumpty" during the year, come back to "The Giant Leap" and read it again for this bit of literary analysis.

Following the dialogue in this "cartoon-strip" illustration might not be an easy task for some children, so give help as you see it's needed.

8

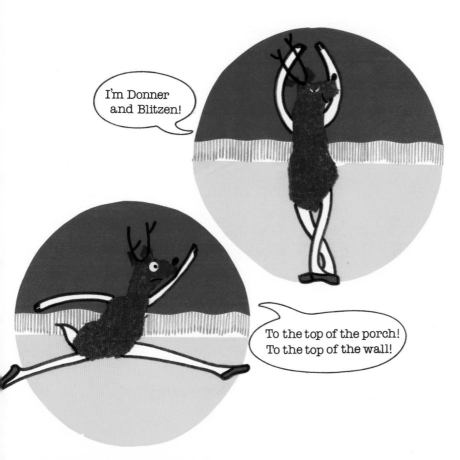

If any child in your class is studying ballet, he/she would be happy to show and name the various dance positions pictured here. If not, perhaps there's a child somewhere in your school who can demonstrate the ballet positions to your class.

9

This beautifully illustrated, nonfiction scientific piece follows the miracle of the poppy's life cycle. The illustrations show the poppy as a young plant through fertilization by the insect to the release of seeds and replanting.

It's surprising how much scientific information young children absorb by watching their parents' garden, visiting a factory, watching someone work on a car or unload a truck full of furniture. Children in your class, looking at these pictures, can reveal what they know about the life cycle of a plant.

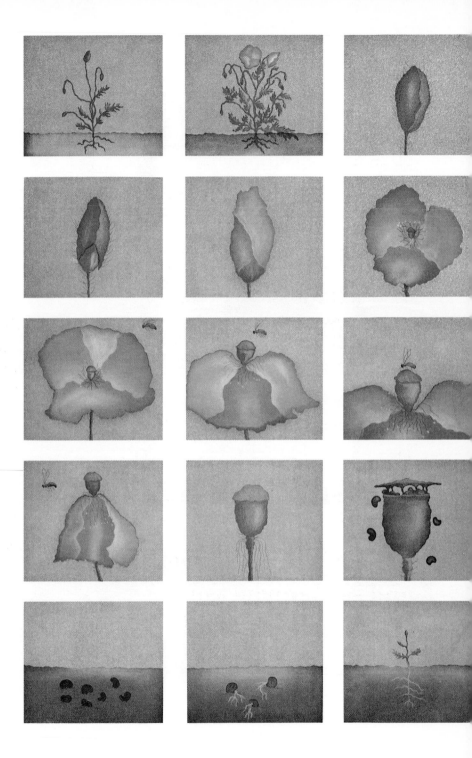

Poppies

by Bill Martin Jr
pictures by Colette

It is a miracle of nature
that a small poppy seed
grows into a plant
that blossoms beautifully
and produces a pouch
of small poppy seeds.

Each new seed
then produces a plant
that blossoms beautifully
and produces still more seeds.

The growing, blossoming,
and seed production
go on and on and on,
year after year.

Don't worry about the vocabulary and conceptual load of the text. Children, of necessity, have learned how to accommodate and approximate. Anything they don't understand, they tune out. If what they tune out leaves a hole in the middle of what they understand, they fill it up with some logical thinking.

The more children hear you read the text aloud, the better they will understand it. Rather than reading it through ten times on one day, it is better to read it one time a day for ten days.

You might also want to discuss other cyclical events in nature, such as night and day, the seasons, weather, sunrise and sunset, etc.

11

On Top

by Tom Glazer

On top of spaghetti

I lost my poor meatball

It rolled off the table

And then my poor meatball

paghetti

ctures

Peter Lippman

all covered with cheese,

when somebody sneezed.

and onto the floor,

rolled out of the door.

The way in which the words of the song are laid out on these two pages seems to defy convention. The words move across both pages, all the way from left to right, then back to the left, and so on. The wonder is that children have little difficulty with this layout because they are always seeking the sound of sense. If what they read doesn't make sense, they try reading it another way. You can help them by pointing to the text as you read it the first few times.

Don't be surprised if this proves to be the children's favorite song, story, poem, art—everything. They like funny things and this is top-of-the-chart!

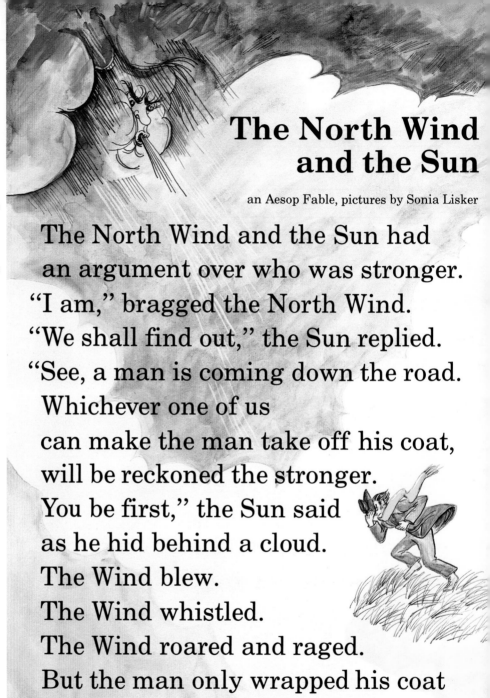

The North Wind and the Sun

an Aesop Fable, pictures by Sonia Lisker

The North Wind and the Sun had
an argument over who was stronger.
"I am," bragged the North Wind.
"We shall find out," the Sun replied.
"See, a man is coming down the road.
Whichever one of us
can make the man take off his coat,
will be reckoned the stronger.
You be first," the Sun said
as he hid behind a cloud.
The Wind blew.
The Wind whistled.
The Wind roared and raged.
But the man only wrapped his coat
more closely about himself.

By reading other
versions of this fable
to the children, they
can enjoy making
comparisons, finding
ways they are alike
and different.

This simple story is
excellent for
dramatizing or
miming.

My turn now," said the Sun.
Coming out from behind the cloud,
the Sun shone gently.
The man unbuttoned his coat.
Then the Sun shone warmer,
and the man loosened his coat.
The Sun shone still warmer
until the man was so hot,
he took off his coat and sat down
under the shade of a tree.

The Sun had won with gentleness
what the Wind could not with force.

This is an old song used as a reading game for children.

There probably was never a better phonics lesson than on these two pages! This song motivates children to use all of their reasoning powers to find rhyming words and gives them the satisfaction of being successful. Challenge them to create additional combinations of their own.

plane over a train

goat wearing a coat

whale wagging its tail

cat swinging a bat

bee on a thre

bear combing its hair

two ants doing a dance

clown reading upside do

cow pulling a plow

fish throwing a dish

dog sawing a log

fox wearing socks

duck driving a truck

Down by the Bay

where the watermelons grow

back to my home

I dare not go

for if I do

my mother will say,

"Did you ever see a pig

dancing a jig?"

down by the bay.

an old camp song   pictures by Michael and Mark Foreman

dragon pulling a wagon

mouse painting a house

Cat-in-the-Tree

by John Archambault
pictures by Steven Kellogg

Here's a story poem that is within the experience of most children. Read it once a day for several days, and in no time at all, the children will be saying it with you. There are some tricky phrases and an unusual rhythm, but that won't deter them. Children are master language learners.

The pictures for this selection are by Steven Kellogg who also illustrated the cover, title page, and first story in the book. Aren't they lovely?

Skit, scat, scootle doot,
Diddle, diddle dee,
The dog chased the cat
Up the sycamore tree.

"Meow-meow-meow,"
Said the Cat-in-the-Tree,
"Poky little puppy Lyle
Couldn't catch me!"

"Bow-wow-wow,"
Said Dog-on-the-Ground,
"Come down, Lady fraidy cat,
Meet me on the ground."

18

I'm fine where I am,"
Said Cat-in-the-Tree,
Won't you please come up
And dine with me?

Bring along
your bone,
We'll have
catnip tea!"

These old jingles have appealed to children from the moment they were created. Chime them and chant them and in no time the children will be chanting them with you. You will find them repeating these delightful jumprope rhymes throughout the day, in the classroom and on the playground. And how proud they will be to point to one of the jingles on the page and tell you, "I know that! I can read it!"

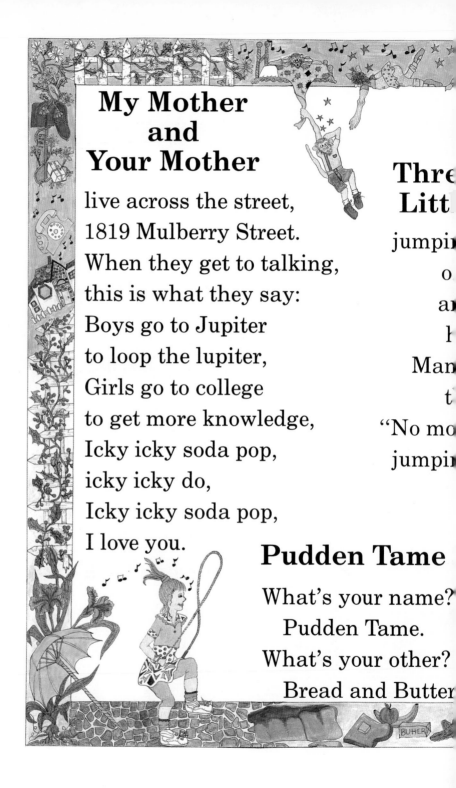

My Mother and Your Mother

live across the street,
1819 Mulberry Street.
When they get to talking,
this is what they say:
Boys go to Jupiter
to loop the lupiter,
Girls go to college
to get more knowledge,
Icky icky soda pop,
icky icky do,
Icky icky soda pop,
I love you.

Thre Litt

jumpi
o
a
h
Man
t
"No mo
jumpi

Pudden Tame

What's your name?
Pudden Tame.
What's your other?
Bread and Butter

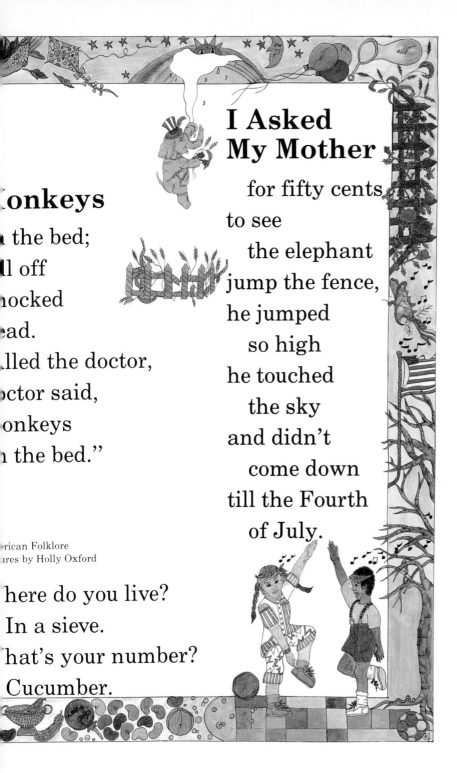

onkeys

the bed;
ll off
hocked
ead.
lled the doctor,
octor said,
onkeys
the bed."

rican Folklore
res by Holly Oxford

here do you live?
In a sieve.
hat's your number?
Cucumber.

I Asked My Mother

for fifty cents
to see
   the elephant
jump the fence,
he jumped
   so high
he touched
   the sky
and didn't
   come down
till the Fourth
   of July.

Fine art orders the chaos of the world and helps us see things clearly, without confusion. It's amazing how Michael Foreman reduced the landscape and gave us a great span of sky bordered by leaves of neighboring trees and a garland of flowers entwining the swing. Michael Foreman is one of the foremost children's book illustrators in the world. The complete elegance of this illustration makes it very special.

THE SWING

by Robert Louis Stevenson
pictures by Michael Foreman

How do you like to go up in a swing,
Up in the air so blue?
Oh, I do think it is the pleasantest thing
Ever a child can do!

Up in the air and over the wall,
Till I can see so wide,
Rivers and trees and cattle and all
Over the countryside—

And what do you know! The cow is now jumping over the wind-blown leaves!

22

Till I look down on the garden green,
Down on the roof so brown—
Up in the air I go flying again,
Up in the air and down!

Whose Mouse Are You?

This is perhaps the best novel ever written for young children. Just consider the situation: a little mouse whose mother is inside a cat, whose father is caught in a trap, whose sister has run away, and who doesn't have a brother. But guess what—this little mouse has courage and overcomes all obstacles and gets a baby brother in the bargain. What a success story!

Children love this story and you can easily read it together. You read the red text and they read the black. You will find them reading and dramatizing the story over and over.

The marvelous illustrations by Jose Aruego are deceptively simple. They reveal the character of a very strong, determined mouse.

Whose mouse are you?

Nobody's mouse.

Where is your mother?

Inside the cat.

by Robert Kraus

24

Where is your father?

Caught in a trap.

Where is your sister?

Far from home.

Where is your brother?

I have none.

This story might remind the children of other children's stories with creative, industrious characters—*Are You My Mother?* by P. D. Eastman, *If You Give a Mouse a Cookie* by Laura Numeroff, and *The Story of a Little Mouse Trapped in a Book* by Monique Felix.

 pictures by Jose Aruego

What will you do?

Shake my mother
out of the cat!

Free my father
from the trap!

Find my sister
and bring her home.

Wish for a brother
as I have none.

Now whose mouse are you?

My mother's mouse,
          she loves me so.

My father's mouse,
          from head to toe.

My sister's mouse,
          she loves me too.

My brother's mouse . . .

Your brother's mouse?

My brother's mouse —

he's brand new!

Here's Noodles! Noodles can have a birthday whenever you want. Why don't you plan a class party for him. If your children would like to send a birthday card to Noodles, his address is *Reading Editor, DLM Inc, 1 DLM Park, Allen, TX 75002.*

30

After a few weeks, the children will know every selection in this book by heart. However, each selection will bear repetition throughout the year. Children learn to read by reading—primarily by reading the familiar. Their power over the page and knowing exactly what it says, gives them the freedom to role-play the act of reading. It also gives them confidence in analyzing individual words and finding letters they know.

The children will enjoy awarding their own Newbery medal for their favorite selection and Caldecott medal for their favorite illustration.

Happy birthday to you,
Happy birthday to you,
Happy birthday, dear Noodles,
Happy birthday to you.

a traditional song
picture by George Buckett

31

What is Noodles doing now?
Hello, Noodles!

Bill Martin's
Sounds of Language
Readers

Sounds of Children at Play on the Hill
Sounds Around the Mountain
Sounds of an Owly Night
Sounds of Home
Sounds of Numbers
Sounds Around the Clock
Sounds of a Powwow
Sounds of Laughter

Acknowledgments
Cover painting by Steven Kellogg

With thanks and appreciation to International Telecharge, Inc. for permission to use the painting, "Dinosaur," by Steve Peitzach.

"Watch Out Little Mouse" from *In the Middle of the Night* by Aileen Fisher. Copyright © 1965 by Aileen Fisher. (T.Y. Crowell) Reprinted by permission of Harper & Row, Publishers, Inc.

With thanks to the Whole Language Consultants of Winnepeg, Manitoba, Canada, for permission to use the "Great Gray Owl" art by Terry Gallagher, copyright 1986.

"The Lion Sleeps Tonight" (Wimoweh) (Mbube) New lyrics and revised music by Hugo Peretti, Luigi Creatore, George Weiss, and Albert Stanton. Based on a song by Solomon Linda and Paul Campbell. TRO copyright © 1951 Folkways Music Publishers, Inc., New York, N.Y. (Renewed) 1952 (Renewed) and 1961 (Renewed) Folkways Music Publishers, Inc., New York, N.Y. All rights reserved. Used by permission.

With special thanks to Linda Ross, Vice President, Editorial, and Carol Misiaszek, Production Manager DLM.

Acknowledgment is made to Betty Jean Mitchell, for permission to use the character, Noodles, copyright © 1981.

Every effort has been made to locate and secure permissions from the copyright holders for the stories used in this book. The publishers will be grateful if any omissions or errors are brought to their attention for correction.

Bill Martin's SOUNDS OF LANGUAGE

An Essay for Teachers

One DLM Park • Allen, Texas 75002

Here, good teachers,
is the new *Sounds of Language*—
well, not altogether new.
Selections from prior editions of the program
have been carefully blended with new works
to make this series appropriate
for use in your classrooms today
and, we hope, for many tomorrows.

This teacher's essay has two sections.
The first is a philosophical statement
about children and teaching.

The second part is a discussion of strategies
for helping children
develop awareness and appreciation
for the workings of literature and language,
placing you in a vibrant partnership
with children, books, and literacy learning.
It's a demanding assignment
leavened with creativity,
daily satisfactions,
worthwhile purposes,
and more fun
than teaching has ever been.

Part One
The Philosophy of
Sounds of Language

The *Sounds of Language* reading program
is a fresh and enchanting collection
of poems, stories, songs, articles, and pictures
that realistically prompts children
to hear the spoken patterns
of the sentences they read.
As children gain skill in using their ears
to guide their eyes in reading,
they have a qualitatively different reading experience.

Consider young children
who have frequently heard a teacher read
a favorite childhood poem or story.
Once children have the sounds of that selection
clearly and solidly in the ear,
they have little difficulty
reading the piece in its printed form.
As the ears begin telling
what the eyes are seeing,
reading becomes a task that children do
with confidence and expectation.

"I know that word!
That word is 'little!' "

There is the evidence that the child
is relating sight and sound in reading.

Children, from birth,
have been beginning to figure out how language works
and how to make it work for them.
At each level
in the *Sounds of Language* program,
children are continually helped to become aware
of what they intuitively know about language.
They are helped to explore
and verbalize old and new learnings.

Sounds of Language
is a total linguistic and aesthetic experience
that logically and comfortably connects
children's oral language ability
with their intuitive knowledge of how language works.

It premises that language is life,
that "I am my language, my language is me."
It assumes the responsibility
for releasing children
to their maximum language potential.

The program can be used effectively
in several different and simultaneous ways.

1) It can be used as a bridging instrument
   for teachers wanting to move
   from a teacher-centered reading program
   to a child-centered language program
   in which learning is a creative,
   self-generated process.
2) It can be used to help children
   learning English as a second language,
   inculcating the melodies, cadences, words, and meanings
   embedded in the sentence sounds of language.
3) It can be used by children already experienced
   in the power and productivity of reading
   as an anthology of playful, literary selections
   that they will turn to again and again
   simply because they enjoy
   the life-enhancing experience
   of reading the familiar.

The program has no prescribed sets of questions
to be asked about a given selection.
It makes no presumptions about the course
a class discussion or group activity will take.
It offers no vocabulary lists to be pre- or post-taught.
It presents no absolutes to be learned.

Sounds of Language presumes
that the classroom quest
for meaning and linguistic awareness
during or following the reading of a selection
is mediated by children's responses
and the teacher's sensitivity to those responses.
Children's curiosities and insights, therefore,
form the "lesson plan."

This places you, the teacher,
in the role of observer
as children engage in the lifelong process
of finding meaning in whatever they do
and translating that meaning into language.
Your best participation is that of a guide and appreciator,
always ready to validate children's eagerness and efforts
as they become increasingly aware
of what they intuitively know
about language and about life.

The pages of the pupil's book
incorporated in this teacher's edition
have been annotated for your convenience.
Annotations appear where they are needed
to point up learning insights and teaching suggestions.

The annotations printed in red
relate to the literary features of the selection.
The annotations printed in blue
point out linguistic features and
suggest activities that emerge from the literature
to inculcate language skills in the developing reader.
Thoughtful care has been given to the annotations
so that their presence will help you
use *Sounds of Language* to the utmost through:
1) helping with language analysis,
   literary appreciation, and child development;
2) pointing out key learnings that relate to
   mathematics, science, social studies, and writing;
3) suggesting ways to use selections
   for independent study activities;
4) outlining ways to use the books
   as language resources;
5) engaging children in thinking
   and problem solving activities;
6) fostering an understanding and appreciation of art;
7) making up a complete program of
   choral speaking and reading;
8) developing practical ways
   to release children's ideas and feelings
   through open-ended questions
   and personalized discussions;
9) presenting achievement measures based on
   actual performance with language,
   rather than artificial testing methods; and,
10) offering ideas for useful at-home
    or out-of-class activities.

At no time is an annotation so prescriptive
that it precludes your own insight
and experience with the teaching process.
To the contrary,
the annotations are geared to trigger
all your insights and hunches
about helping children latch on to language and,
indeed, to their humanity.

The philosophical premises on
which *Sounds of Language* is based
are the undergirdings that can free you
to follow the edicts of your heart and mind
in working effectively with young language learners.
There are three of them:
    1) All children are language experts.
    2) Language works in chunks of meaning.
    3) Teacher language creates a powerful environment.

All Children Are Language Experts

All healthily-born children
have two concomitant needs:
    1) the need for food and care, and
    2) the need for language.
Food and care are necessary to sustain children
until they can care for themselves;
language is necessary
to provide membership in the human community.
The two needs are equally urgent.
One without the other
is a distortion of the norm.
The first need must be satisfied for children,
but the second need is fulfilled by children themselves.
It is they who teach themselves
to talk, to discourse, to communicate.

Using their innate language endowment,
newborn babies encapsule meaning in their various cries—
    "I'm hungry!"
    "I'm sick!"
    "I'm stuck by a pin!"
In euphoric moments,
babies babble, coo, gurgle, and drool,
    "I'm happy."
    "I'm comforted."
    "I'm at peace in my world."

Immediately after birth, children
start attending to the cacophony of sound about them.
In less time than it takes most five-year-olds
to learn "the vowel sounds,"
these wee ones learn—without a teacher—
the sounds of the father's voice,
the mother's voice,
the siblings',
the sitter's.
They differentiate mechanical and human sounds
(no child ever tried to produce the sound of an air conditioner).
By trial and error,
with unflagging energy,
they learn the native language—
the vocabulary,
the syntax,
the meanings,
the intonations,
the cadences,
the whole
"wild"
inconsistent,
contradictory,
circumstantial
ways of language working.
It has nothing to do with race, creed, color, or IQ.

All normal, healthy children the world over,
become language users
in the same way and at approximately the same time.
At age three, or thereabout,
children begin speaking in sentences,
the greatest intellectualism of a lifetime,
giving each utterance
the proper melody and intended meaning,
putting each word in the necessary hierarchical position,
improvising with linguistic insight
such utterances as
    "It's amazable" and
    "I runned home."

At age five or earlier,
these geniuses come into our classrooms
speaking, understanding, and improvising language
for every conceivable purpose.
Language has become the way of life.
Children are walking language laboratories.
They use every kind of sentence indigenous to the culture:
the simple sentence,
the compound,
the complex,
the declarative,
the imperative,
the implied,
the incomplete, and, of course,
the ubiquitous run-on.

Their beings are filled with words,
with combinations of words,
with thoughts and the ability to translate those thoughts
into language that fits the situation,
with values that ultimately determine
their physical, emotional, and cognitive behavior.

Do these language bearers,
these print detectives,
suddenly need reading instruction
to make a go of reading and writing?
Do these creative, brilliant language-producers
need only skill texts and ditto sheets?
No, no, no!
What they need is an array
of evocative, personally satisfying books,
an agenda of literacy concerns
of their own deriving,
and a head full of stirring dreams to beckon them on.

They need the tools of literacy—
papers and
pencils and
paints and
printing machines.
They need a supportive environment
that focuses their communicative talents
into blocks of time
necessary for thoughtful expression.

They need books,
books from wide-ranging sources.
The classroom that is filled
with books of all kinds,
from school libraries,
from public libraries,
from children's homes,
from your personal collection,
from bookstores, or
from wherever they may be found
is a classroom that is ripe
for linguistic development and evolution.
Books house the treasury
of humanity's knowledge,
language, and dreams.
They provide the best vehicle
for endowing children
with the rich cultural heritage
that is theirs to share.

Most of all,
they need teachers
who can identify and challenge their geniuses.
For there are no dumb children
unless an authoritative classroom
or some other authoritative source
has condemned them to silence.

Language Works
in Chunks of Meaning

As each of us learned to speak the language,
we learned to cluster words into meaningful units.
Even as babbling babies,
we used intonation and clustering
to create a sound of sense.
Later, as we learned vocabulary and sentence ways,
we made full use of sentence sounds
(sometimes called melodies),
demonstrating that we intuitively understood
that language works in chunks of meaning.

Not one of us said,
   "I (pause) want (pause) my (pause) mommy!"
Rather
   "Iwanmymommy!"
came out as a meaningful linguistic whole,
a fluid sentence sound with a cultural melody
that conveyed both feeling and thought.

In similar ways
we instinctively speak and read
"Once upon a time. . ."
as a linguistic chunk that bears meaning.
We think it,
utter it,
understand it
as *one* word,
not four words.

Good readers need only glimpses
at the cargo-bearing words
to immediately release
chunks of meaning that shape a sentence:

> Once ___ ___ ___
> ___ ___ ___ ___ lady
> ___ ___ ___ ___ cottage
> ___ ___ river.

The meaningful sentence becomes:

> Once upon a time
> there was an old lady
> who lived in a cottage
> by the river.

Rapid readers look for the cargo words,
not the glue words in a sentence
or in a paragraph.
It is the cargo words that release the chunks of meaning.
Naturally, rapid readers make many miscues,
but they feel free to risk
because most of their miscues have little bearing
on their understanding of the message.
When a miscue derails the experienced reader
from understanding the author,
the reader stops and re-reads
as many sentences or paragraphs as necessary
to get "back on the author's track."
Re-reading to correct or to ferret out an elusive meaning
is the hallmark of an educated reader.

Our oral language
is uttered in chunks of meaning
without our thinking about it.
Only when we are self-doubtful
and feeling inadequate
do we stammer through a sentence
word by word.

The poets, more than anyone else in our society,
have tended to improve
the communication potential of their writing
by arranging their words into natural linguistic clusters.

Observe how Robert Frost
accommodates the lines in "October"
to chunks of meaning.

O hushed October,
morning mild,
thy leaves have ripened
to the fall.
Tomorrow's wind,
if it be wild,
could waste them all.

A page of prose in an ordinary book
moves rigidly, line by line,
from a left-hand margin to a right-hand margin
with only the paragraph breaks.
This inflexible technique severs words in half
in order to accommodate the margins
and ignores the natural clustering of words
in chunks of meaning
within each sentence.
Experienced readers
have mastered the printing conventions
of the book form,
but inexperienced readers,
particularly children,
can become stressed and enfeebled
by the inflexibility of print.

Let's see what a prose sentence written by Bernard Martin
would look like if it were separated
into its chunks of meaning
to enhance the linguistic design of the sentence
rather than the arbitrary width of the page.

Sometimes the male lions may help ambush the
game, but more often they take their rest under
shady trees and watch while the lionesses stalk
and kill the game that will become a feast for
all of the lions.

King of Beasts

This complex sentence
becomes much easier to read
when it is printed in its chunks of meaning.

Sometimes the male lions
may help ambush the game,
but more often
they take their rest
under shady trees
and watch
while the lionesses stalk
and kill the game
that will become a feast
for all of the lions.

Each group of words has a meaning
that is more important
than any single word within the group.
The words in each group, therefore,
must be read together
as a subset of the more important set—
the entire sentence.
Each subset leads into the next,
gradually amalgamating
into the larger meaning of the sentence.
One of the miracles of language is
its way of working in chunks of meaning.

Throughout *Sounds of Language*
we have arranged the print in chunks of meaning
to facilitate the reading
and to help children intuit how language works.

Reading instruction that emphasizes
single
word
recognition
above
all
else
actually creates reading problems for children
because units of meaning
are rudely torn apart.

Children soon learn that word-by-word reading
is what the teacher approves.
From the beginning
reading in chunks of meaning
should be modeled and expected of all children.
Children should be freed
to use their accumulated linguistic insights
in handling the "hard" words:
skip them or
use a word that seems to make sense.
The concept of chunks of meaning
is not foreign to children.
They naturally speak in chunks of meaning
as they frame their oral sentences.
They need only to be helped to see
that they can find similar chunks
on the printed page,
even though most books are printed in paragraph form.
Hopefully, the day will come when books,
at least for elementary school children,
will have considerable material
printed in chunks of meaning.

Teacher Language Creates a Powerful Environment

Regardless of subject matter,
language is the educational province.
Wisely or poorly used,
it shuttles substance into the warp and woof
of inner and outer existence.
It can lace the user into captivity
just as surely as it can weave new designs of freedom.
Therein is a danger—and an opportunity.
Teacher language itself creates a powerful environment,
in which both you and the children
grow and develop together
as human beings involved in the quest for meaning.
Ideally, it frees you and the children
to accept yourselves and accomplish your purposes.
Ideally, it supports your individualized ways
of thinking and being.

Some children we have known
seemed at first to read more with their feet
than they did with their eyes.
You've had children like these in your own classrooms.
Aren't they interesting as they screw themselves up
into impossible positions
and keep perfect time to whatever is being read?

We should be saying to these children:
   "You're so great at reading with your feet!
      How would you like to try reading with your eyes?"

And they wouldn't mind at all—
in fact they might be delighted to try—
knowing their comfortable methods
for responding to print
have been so highly respected
by positive teacher language.
But unfortunately,
we don't usually recognize rhythmical body response
as acceptable reading behavior,
accustomed as we are
to thinking about reading
as an eye exercise
and a "sounding-out" ritual.

Consider the environment
in which
there comes the repeated admonition:
   "Now, children, sit up straight
      and pay attention to your book."

If these children had the skill of self-analysis
and dared challenge the teacher's linguistic edict,
they might respond:
    "But I am paying attention.
    Rhythmical body response
    is part of reading a book."

Only they probably don't have the language
to verbalize their intuitive response to print.
Powerful teacher language
that condemns their reading behavior
is inappropriate.
It could start potentially successful readers
on a long and uncomfortable journey to reading failure,
and it could throw another potentially fine teacher
into miscommunication with children
simply because the definition of reading behavior
and the perceived language to be used in the classroom
are too narrow
to accept and encourage
the many-faceted reading behavior
of real live children.

We've come to believe
that the tooling of language
to support and release children
in their maturation
is the most significant characteristic of good teaching.
In this context, teaching is not "teaching" at all.
It is an act of guiding and appreciating.
It carries the thrust of intimate familiarity
with curriculum goals and cultural expectancies,
with subject matter and skill delineations,
with conceptual developments and aesthetic interrelations—
but of even greater value
is its generosity of taste,
its supportive patience and abundant caring,
its pervasive geniality and appetite for living.
In the constancy of an optimum linguistic environment,
the teacher and children come together day after day
with easy assurance and high-level energy,
joyfully committed to the job at hand,
and confident that they will succeed.

Hopefully, *Sounds of Language*
models the positive influence of literary language
in the classroom.

Part Two
Teaching with
Sounds of Language

Now, let's talk about ways
for using *Sounds of Language*
to bring new dimensions
into your teaching of reading.
We have no choice but to help
all children learn to read.
They inherit the need to read
simply by living in our culture.
We, therefore, have the obligation to provide
wide-ranging ways for unlocking print
and for engaging in the literary experience.

Experiencing literature as a reader or a listener
is only a first step in "possessing the experience."
As John Dewey believed:
    We play,
    but we experience the play
    by talking about it.

The children in your classrooms
are not uninitiated learners.
They are superb learners,
ranking self-instructors,
mental, physical, and emotional forces
who can learn anything they wish.

As my mentor and friend, Paul Witty, always said,
    "We don't have to teach children reading skills.
      If we can ascertain their interests
        and provide materials that feed into those interests,
      children will do their own teaching."

The art of determining a child's interests
and designing activities that encompass those interests
is the art of good teaching.
As Yetta Goodman says,
    "It takes a lot of kid watching."

Releasing children to their own
styles and patterns of learning
is not learned in college methods books.
It is learned by caring for children,
caring so much that it could be called "loving"—
for the ultimate teaching technique is love.

Children learn best and most efficiently
from teachers they love and respect—
from teachers who love and respect them.

The teaching methods of *Sounds of Language*
are purposefully open-ended
so that teachers can use
the fullness of the teaching art
that they individually possess.
Just as we believe that children should be encouraged
to experience the play of linguistic awareness
as dictated by their own developmental sequence
and the creative human interaction that literature provides,
so we believe that teachers should have the opportunity
to develop a teaching style and methodology
that reflect personal growth and evolution
of the understandings and appreciations
that are embedded in the linguistic heritage.

The steps to using *Sounds of Language*
to the best advantage
grow out of three basic assumptions:
1) Linguistic awareness requires nurturing.
2) Reading aloud deposits literary and linguistic structures
   in children's memories.
3) Improvisations, growing out of a literary experience,
   are the best way to cement and focus the learning.

The first step cultivates children's readiness
to read or to listen or to do.
We can't assume that children,
left to their own devices,
are properly motivated,
day in and day out.
Their intensity, purpose, and concentration
need constant cultivation.

The teacher possesses the responsibility
and the implements to provide support.
The teacher must have more of a guide
than merely a curriculum outline;
more than simply words in a book.
Words alone, in whatever context,
are but weak reeds to lean on.
A better support is the carefully moderated,
constantly maintained belief
that every child has enormous ability
to get uniquely involved in each situation.

We teachers do our best work by giving children
the opportunities to be involved.
Just use your finely focused professional intelligence,
finding delight in sharing with children,
in discussing with them,
in planning, considering, and anticipating
what they might do.

Don't fret about it,
although every good teacher we know
does a lot of fretting about children
and about teaching procedures.
Good luck!

The second step in the teaching process is easier.
Give children a road map by reading aloud to them.
When children hear, for example,
a treasured poem read aloud,
they can experience its cadences, its rhyme, its emphases
without having to experience all the byways on their own.
Their more intimate explorations will come later,
perhaps much later in their lives,
after they have acquired a real love of literature
and a desire for scholarly perfection.
It is enough, for now, that they sense in you
the scholarly modeling that demonstrates
the way a poem finds its way
from the ear and the eye
to the heart and the brain.

A chosen poem or other literary piece
can be read aloud many times,
preferably once a day for ten days
rather than ten times in one day.

In short time, children will chime in
with your reading,
accelerating the process of
moving the language
from the ear to long-term memory.

Then comes the third step.
Deciding how to involve the children,
how to encourage them to respond creatively,
how to encourage them to literary improvisation.
Learning is a game of quick episodes.
The intensity, energy, and expectation
that children bring to a poem,
for example, has to be nurtured into another phase.
Your belief in their creative abilities
and the joy that you find in that belief
are the fertility for children's learning.
This change you're asking of children—
from learners to creators—
is the third phase of good teaching.

We do not tell a child or a group of children what to do.
We suggest.
> "Mahadeo, you're good at drawing.
>   Maybe you heard a picture in the poem
>   that you would like to paint."

"Avis, you're a talented calligrapher.
  Maybe you would like to print the poem
  on a big sheet to hang on the wall
  for all in the class to read together."

"Who's the language expert who would
  like to make up a new title
  for our favorite story 'Avocado Baby'?
  It will be a tough job to convince us
  that a new title is better
  because we are so familiar
  with the title given to it
  by the author, John Burningham."

Children who are doing what they want to do
and what they do best
will never get bored.
Moreover, children who are intent
on doing "their thing"
don't need a teacher—
they need an audience.
At this point, your role has changed,
from challenger and instigator
to appreciator and validator.

Step One:
Linguistic Awareness
Requires Nurturing

The content of *Sounds of Language*
is specifically planned
to place literary appreciation
at the heart of the reading program.
From the very first day of school
throughout the entire school experience,
children using *Sounds of Language*
will be living in the midst of a chorus of literature
and a gallery of contemporary art.
And they will be nurtured
in a climate of literary appreciation
that sensitizes their responses
and imprints their memories
with high idealism and soul-stirring emotions.
Aesthetic response can only be nurtured.
It cannot be taught.

We nurture and motivate children best
by sharing our enthusiasm and anticipated pleasure
in what they will experience in the assignment at hand.
We must give them glimpses
of satisfactions and successes
they will find in the learning encounter.

"Children, this is one of my favorite poems.
I was only four years old
when my grandmother first read it to me,
and I have loved it ever since.
It is also one of Meena's favorite poems.
(Meena is a child in the classroom.)
She told me so yesterday.
Meena, would you like to read it aloud
as the rest of us follow along
in this big book?"

"Chaddy Tod, you're a baseball fan.
You read box scores like a pro.
Would you like to show those of us
who aren't so familiar with baseball and box scores
what all the abbreviations and numbers mean?
Twila's mother made us this big box score chart.
You must be very proud of your mother, Twila.
She's a fine artist and so generous
for helping us whenever we ask."

By a wide and continuing exposure
to stories, poems, art, photos, essays,
and other moments that possess
some pretension to taste,
children will begin to know
what they do and do not like.
Knowing what one does not like
is equally as important as knowing what one enjoys.

Whatever else, a child's response must be self-selected
and it must be sincere.
We teachers need to learn
how to live with children's responses
that move against the grain
of our own preferences
and that reveal pleasure in the mundane.
Many children will necessarily go through
a long period of literary exposure
before they are apt to sense the worthwhileness
of Emily Dickinson's poem "Autumn"
as compared to the joy they find
in their favorite "knock-knock" jokes.
Be assured that those pleasurable times of the day
when you read aloud to children
are all a part of a program
in literary and aesthetic appreciation,
as well as a part of the reading program.

There is a character,
a recurring character named Noodles,
who literally flits in and out
of all of the *Sounds of Language* books.
Noodles is the essence of every child.
Noodles both embodies and empowers
the interests and fascinations of children
as they approach new language,
new literature, new experiences,
and new excitement.

Noodles may share a fleeting moment
of fun and frolic with a friend.
Noodles may speak for children,
expressing their apprehension
or their unbridled curiosity
about the conceptual, linguistic,
and situational newness and wonder
that you are presenting to them.
Noodles is the child within every human
who is not afraid to take risks,
not afraid to be wrong,
not afraid to taste new delights,
not afraid to question,
not afraid to be.
You can use Noodles' appearances
throughout the program
to motivate and challenge,
to comfort and console,
to reassure, and to reflect
children in your care.

Children develop many life areas simultaneously.
They move quickly from one set of interests to another.
Capturing those interests
and developing thematic units of action
help children cultivate
their purposeful use of language.
Whether it is raising a guinea pig,
observing an angelfish,
visiting a museum display of dinosaurs,
tasting a new food,
experiencing an unfamiliar weather phenomenon,
gaining a new brother or sister,
or discovering a mysteriously shaped rock—
anything can spur children's interest.
Use those interests, the *Sounds of Language*,
and any other linguistic resource available
to weave literature and language
into the classroom explorations.
Browse through all of the books
for selections that fit the mood.
These books do not have to be read
page by page from cover to cover.
You can pick and choose from anywhere in the book,
depending on the interests and purposes
of the children and yourself.

Step Two: Reading Aloud Deposits Literary and Linguistic Structures in Children's Memories

Reading aloud to children sensitizes them
to patterns of words that repeat
over and over in our language;
it skyrockets certain individual words
into a burst of awareness that lasts a lifetime;
it tunes children's ears to the pronunciation of words
and to the cadence of various kinds of sentences
in ways that print itself cannot;
it develops a special kind of kinship
between the teacher and the children
and between the children and the literature
that helps children know why reading is important.

Each of us has a linguistic storehouse
into which we deposit patterns
for stories
and poems
and sentences
and words.

These patterns enter the memory through the ear
and remain available, ready to be cued into action,
throughout the whole of a lifetime,
providing advance information that is valuable
for reading, writing, speaking, listening, and thinking.

The good reader is a person
who looks at a page of print
and begins recalling patterns
that have been stored in the linguistic treasury.

These patterns range
all the way from the plot structure
an author has used in a story
to the rhyme scheme that hangs a poem together,
to the placement of an adjective
in front of a noun
as part of the shape of a sentence,
to the underlying rhythmical structure
in a line of prose or poetry,
to the -ed ending
as part of the shape of a word.
As these various kinds of structures
are triggered into play,
good readers are able to figure out
the similarity between a new structure
and structures already claimed.

Poor readers are persons who,
looking at a page of print,
find no patterns that trigger information
to help them unlock the page.
This lack of triggering also occurs
if the oral language patterns are not the kind
that are encountered in print.
Children whose first language
is not English, for example,
have stored sentence patterns
that generally do not help unlock English sentences.
But these children can be helped
by being read to day after day
in and out of the classroom.
As they hear and store
the typical shape and melodies of English sentences
they become more able to read and write English print.

Reading aloud, over and over,
always a genuine delight,
to children at every level,
of all ages,
is a continuing part of the learning
Sounds of Language offers.
It juxtaposes a child's linguistic remembrances
and the reading of print.
It is the best—*the very best*—way
of helping children latch on to reading.

Sometimes you read aloud
and the children listen,
sometimes you read aloud
and the children chime in,
sometimes the children read in chorus,
sometimes the children read aloud in dialogue,
sometimes the children chorus a poem or story by memory,
sometimes you and the children read aloud together,
with the children following the print in their books
so their eyes can be seeing
what their ears are hearing and
what their tongues are saying.

Dust
of Snow

The   way a crow
Shook down on me
The dust of snow
From a hemlock tree

Has given my heart
A change of mood
And saved some part
Of a day I had rued.

Children who have frequently heard
and later read and chorused aloud "Dust of Snow"
will have deposited within the linguistic treasury
a feeling for the sound and meaning of the word *rued*.

Potential use of the word in all kinds of communication—
reading, writing, speaking, and listening—
has been enhanced by the familiarity they have
with this Robert Frost poem.
Moreover, they have the echoing model
of the poet's phrasing and thinking.
There is no better way for children to learn
to use and appreciate our language
than having broad and continuous experiences
that attune both the ear and the tongue—
and later the eye—
to the rhythms, melodies, and sounds of language.

Hopefully, this reading aloud
and language consolidation
will be accompanied by spontaneous body movement—
either the kind of swaying and clapping
that children initiate on their own
or interesting movements suggested by the teacher.
Whenever children engage their entire bodies
in their responses to print,
they have the best possible chance
of intaking linguistic know-how
and bringing wholeness to the reading act.

Yes, there are times in *Sounds of Language*
when children read selections
without having had your read-aloud modeling,
but those occasions are infrequent.
The reason?
Well, *Sounds of Language* is a literary pursuit,
a tuning of responses to the aesthetic line.
Children get so little of that
in traditional reading instruction,
yet it is a highly important need
in the life of a lifelong reader.
The reading of literature,
like other artistic pursuits,
reduces the chaos of randomness
for maximum human impress and pleasure.

> Sing a song of sixpence,
> A pocketful of rye

is as sophisticated and elite
as any two lines could be,
yet this nursery rhyme
with its majestic rhythm and word play
pierces the heart and mind
as forcefully for a 72-year-old
as for a 2-year-old;
as forcefully in the milking shed
as in the university classroom.

By helping children develop an appetite
for the ring of literary language,
we simultaneously strengthen and refine
all of their language abilities.

The *Sounds of Language* program offers
a parade of linguistic pictures chosen
to delight the participant with melodious,
colorful juxtapositions of a favorite medley.
As the individual parts become familiar
and are impressed in the linguistic and visual memories,
children will pick up the books and
read them cover to cover,
matching moods, tones, rhythms, and psychological postures
to the stories as the left-to-right progression moves
from one selection to another.

Whether you are using big books for kindergartners
or smaller-sized books with any age child,
Sounds of Language thrives
on the concept of shared reading.
This essential element of the program
allows teachers and children to interact,
allows literature to be presented,
allows our linguistic heritage to be embodied.
Shared reading makes it possible for a classroom
to become a community of language learners.
Seated close to each other,
the children are also close to the text
and close to the teacher.

Their linguistic enthusiasm, enjoyment,
and appetite are contagious
as they respond to the offering
and the turning of pages:
chiming a poem,
singing a song,
reciting a story,
pondering a question.
It is like a club meeting
where rituals are so well-known
that the slightest clue
sets the literary language afloat
in a finely tuned, intelligent reading.
After the ceremonious procedures,
the tone of the classroom drama changes
to the club's business meeting,
where ideas are discussed,
opinions stated and argued,
choices debated and made,
jokes and reminiscenses shared.
The teacher takes the role of an ally,
a storyteller who reads the selections aloud
with enough frequency that all club members
eventually know them by heart.

No other entry into reading
gives children such immediate participation,
such a dynamic model of what
fluent, insightful oral reading sounds like.
This is the essence of reading aloud.

The quick turning and whisking of pages
inculcates a sense of power over the printed page
and an all-important sense of completion
when the book has run its course
from front to back.

Every child is imbued with the compelling notion that
    "I can read!"

This is the first and only reading skill of any importance.
All else follows.

A friend and first-grade teacher in Edmonton, Alberta,
conditions children throughout the year
to be confident in exploring
a page or more of unfamiliar print.
    "You'll always discover something you know,"
      he tells them,
    "a word,
      a picture,
      a theme,
      an idea,
      a name,
      a relationship,
      a toe-hold of meaning."
That's enough, he says, to assure them
that they are succeeding in their quest for literacy.

Children must be helped to accept their kinship
with language and language ways.

Getting the gist of what is being said
is the *modus operandi*
at every level of communication.
A child's emerging awareness will be personally relevant
whether or not it hinges on the teacher's intentions.

If children are to gain control
of various language experiences
in the *Sounds of Language* program,
they must hear the selections read aloud
frequently enough to insure familiarity with
the ideological and emotional tugs of the selections,
as well as familiarity with the sentence sounds
within the selections.

Hallmark the reading as a playful time.
Be joyously attuned to the selection.
The surest way to kindle that joy
is to approach the selection
as a storyteller, a purveyor of literary delight,
not as a teacher.

Touch a selection lightly,
read it once a day,
or sometimes twice
if the children ask for another go-through.
Or you might ask,
        "Do you want to hear it again?"

But no more than two times through, please—
even that depends on the length of the piece.
Rollicking or poignant selections
that read through in a minute or so
bear repetition,
but much depends on the spirit of play
that we bring to the reading.
When children sense our fun
in reading a particular work,
they identify with us
and often want to pattern the fun
in their own presentations.
Some of the playful aspects
of reading aloud are:
   1) using an exaggerated voice for
      "the dog" or
      "the pig" or
      "the old man" or
      "the bully";
   2) breaking into song if the lines suggest melody;
   3) using body motion at appropriate times,
      such as raising the hand to signal "STOP!"
      or bobbing the head dolefully to read in mock sorrow;
   4) sounding footsteps in rhythm with marching troops
      or a weary traveler going yet another mile;
   5) taking vocal and physical cues
      from any stand-up comedian or family storyteller;

6) inviting the children to echo your reading
   of a selection (particularly a poem or a song)
   line by line, or
   sentence by sentence, or
   major chunk (of meaning) by major chunk;
7) inviting children to read the selection
   as a reader's theatre,
   assigning parts if that seems appropriate;
8) inviting children to "act out" or mime
   a significant moment in the selection;
9) inviting children to talk about other selections
   (ones they have experienced outside the classroom)
   that the current reading has occasioned in their minds;
10) asking children to make up a song
    to go with the story;
11) seeing who would like to paint a picture
    that the story suggests;
12) finding out who would like to tell the story
    (or say the poem or sing the song)
    tomorrow; and,
13) inviting children to make up a dance
    to go with the story.

The target of all this reading aloud
is to fill each child's language memory
with the lilt of the language pattern
of words that are made into sentences.

Immersion in an oral language environment
is ideal instruction for children
learning English as a second language
and for children who have not developed
a treasury of remembered language that comes
from being read to on a daily basis.
In essence, the *Sounds of Language* program
is meant to have the language-learning impact
that a family storyteller or
a reader-aloud-of-books brings
to wee ones snuggled in the lap
or seated closely by
as the language flows from adult to child
in a loving, secure, and bountiful environment.

Those children who come to school
richly blessed by early years
of literary and book experiences
will not be bored with your reading aloud,
even the reading of the selections they already know.
They'll be chiming in,
reading right along with you,
volunteering their remembrances
and observations and personal alignments.
The children's personal comments
are their reactions and wonderings.

As a general rule,
the first reading aloud of a selection
should not be interrupted
unless you are using the experience
as a skill-building exercise
instead of an opportunity for literary enjoyment.

The story is the thing!
Its finely tuned phrasing
and linguistic juxtapositions,
as well as its story structures
and character interweaving,
are the text for language learning,
for self-revelations, and
for literary acquisitions of all kinds.
The story is the most perfect module for
transferring the culture,
whether *en masse*
or one-to-one.

Step Three:
Improvisations
Cement and Focus Learning

After children have heard you read a selection aloud,
they savor and cement the experience
by transforming it into something else:

        a storytelling,

        a choral reading,

        a reader's theatre,

        a drama,

        a picture,

        a book,

        a paraphrasing,

        a song,

        a dance,

        a pantomime,

        a creed,

        a contest,

        a comparison,

        a poster,

        a slogan,

        a diorama,

        a mobile,

        a bulletin board display,

        a symbolism,

        a creative-imaginative-whatever.

One choice in deciding how to follow-up
your reading aloud of a story or poem
is to invite the children to use the author's pattern
for expressing their own thoughts.
By borrowing the underlying structure
of a poem or story or sentence
that they have come to know,
they are involved in two linguistically sound learnings
as they hang their own ideas on that structure:
  1) They are having intuitive experiences
      with the fact that stories and poems
      do have underlying structures.
  2) They are building a bridge between
      the linguistic facts of their worlds
      and the linguistic facts of the printed page.

The invitation to
    "Write about anything you want to"
may fall heavily on the ears of children
who don't own the basic language structures
to give wings to what they want to say.

Sounds of Language
makes it possible for children
of either rich or meager vocabulary
to find challenge in their new creations
which come about as they innovate
on the dependable structures found in the books.

Your reading table may come alive
with fifteen new books (written by children)
each time you read a story or poem
and invite the children to borrow the structure
and to adorn it with their own thoughts and language.
What a wonderful source of material
the reading table becomes
for the children's independent reading.
Because all of the innovative books
are built on structures that the children
have already claimed in read-aloud times with the books,
the children will not only be able
to read the new books more easily,
but they will be recognizing
how useful a person's knowledge
about underlying structure can be in reading.
Thus, children who have just finished reading
Leland B. Jacobs' classic verse

> Good night, Mr. Beetle,
> Good night, Mr. Fly,
> Good night, Mrs. Ladybug,
> The moon's in the sky.
>
> Good night, Miss Kitten,
> Good night, Mr. Pup,
> I'll see you in the morning
> When the sun comes up.
> *Good Night, Mr. Beetle*

will tend to feel that they are meeting an old friend
when they come upon a child's innovated story

> Merry Christmas, Mr Beetle,
> Merry Christmas, Mr. Fly
> Merry Christmas, Mrs. Lady Bug,
> Santa's in the sky.
>
> Merry Christmas, Miss Kitten,
> Merry Christmas, Mr. Pup,
> I'll see you Christmas morning
> When I open presents up.

Imagine the surprise and delight of a fifth-grade teacher,
who had asked his children to do a piece of writing
that would cause him to see pictures,
when a boy who had been considered an academic dropout
came up with this piece of writing:

> The Frog
>
> The frog in the pond a lony *(lonely)*
> little fellow who lives with
> the pussy wilow and the muss *(moss)*
> who sits on a lilly like a bud wathing *(watching)*
> the ixcitment of the day
> when he sees a giant much bigger
> than his size. He sits riady
> coilled like a spring with bright
> marrbled eys ready to dive

in the water and hid *(hide)* only to
disapear like mggic *(magic)* disgased *(disguised)*
with the polution of a once
lively and active pond.

from Mr. Bredahl's fifth grade,
Roosevelt School, Minot, North Dakota

Where did the writing come from?
It has the ring of a poet,
yet the child obviously didn't copy it from print,
for a poet would have grouped the words
into spoken speech units
that this writing partially lacks.
Is this something this child heard,
deposited in his linguistic storehouse,
and is now utilizing?
Or is it a combination
of his own phrasing and literary language?
The miracle is how beautifully and accurately
this boy has called upon his language storehouse
to fulfill his class assignment.
Luckily, Mr. Bredahl did not feel
that it was cheating or copying or uncreative
to borrow literary lines and/or structure.
This is how a newcomer often creates
a language of depth and beauty,
with a feeling of pride
known to all successful writers.

Gradually, this emergent writer will transform
and in other ways reshape the language he has borrowed.
Meanwhile, in his borrowing, he is role-playing himself
as a distinguished user of language.
He is tuning his ears to the aesthetics,
to the judgments of taste.

Naturally, part of the child's development
of linguistic awareness and language consolidation
includes an understanding
of how words work in our written language.
Children are curious creatures,
and their curiosity often leads them
to explicit wonderings
about the scribbles,
dots,
lines,
circles,
dashes,
shapes, and
squiggles
that make up the words they hear, say, and read.

Word study, when it is used,
should emphasize the retrieval of sentences
in the oral tradition,
not on word recognition.
It should come at a time when the children
have the power of story recall.

The teacher uses a pointer to focus the word
or may write it on the board.
The word may be spelled aloud,
its configuration observed,
its definition explored,
its length and parts discussed,
but not all of these manipulations
should be attempted at once—
only the most relevant features,
those most influenced by the story context.

Again, the caution that has been sounded
throughout this essay
and the annotations in the Teacher's Edition:
word study and story reading do not mix.
Word study is an isolated skill-building exercise.
Reading a story is a form of art,
a pleasure,
a moment of joy.

Word study activities should be playful,
not serious and not "learn this or else!"
Using colored chalk adds emotional delight
as well as better communicative relevancy.

If you believe that certain word study features
are requisite to a child's long-range language growth
and want to reinforce casual word study activities
that naturally emerge from a book encounter,
a two- or three-minute word study emphasis can occur,
but should be well separated from reading the selection.
This would be essentially a chalkboard presentation
beginning with "Remember this morning, children,
when we encountered this word in our reading?
Let's take another look at it."
No attempt is made to rekindle the story context.
No attempt is made to relate it to anything
but interest in the word and its value as such.
Children will absorb whatever is relevant to them
about the word and its particular cuing characteristics.
They will also tune out all of the irrelevancies
with never so much as a second thought.

There is no sequence for word study
in *Sounds of Language.*
All language activities are considered
to be some form of word study
and language learning.

Enlivening language learning
with stories,
poems,
songs,
creeds,
memoirs,
discussion,
dramas,
dance,
painting,
excursions,
history,
facts,
and information
is the surest way that children
come to literacy.

Finally, lest we forget,
the primary purpose of teaching
is to help children claim kinship with humanity.
As you use *Sounds of Language*
to inculcate and foster feelings
of individual worth and high idealism,
you can be assured that you are engaging
in humanly useful language teaching and development.
For it is on the wings of words
that we claim our identity with our culture.
We must help children find access to those words.

If *Sounds of Language* fulfills all of its expectations,
you, and we, and every concerned human being
who has become dedicated to helping children learn,
will have developed a camaraderie
that will change the course
of language instruction in our schools.
Together we can make language truly available to children
in terms of their emerging human needs.